voucher book
for women

KNOCK KNOCK®
VENICE, CALIFORNIA

Welcome Note

Every romantic relationship is like a mini-economy, albeit a rather complicated one. Although no money changes hands, it's difficult to leave a debt unpaid in a relationship. Rewards and penance can't be left outstanding for long. And who knows exactly how to compare the value of cooking a nice meal, cleaning the toilet, or having sex anyway?

This book of vouchers is a wonderful way to simplify the gift economy of love, while adding a bit of fun, too. For example, you could save up your vouchers and spend a weekend on a love binge. How about breakfast in bed, morning coffee, or a special day out?
You'll no longer need to drop subtle hints: a voucher says
(and implies) more than a thousand words ever could.

What's more, the vouchers won't just come in handy
for your partner; you can give them to your friends, too.
"Sorry I forgot your birthday—here's a voucher for
an evening out together!" "Didn't we have a great
time yesterday? Next time, I'll pay!" "Aren't you just
adorable—here's a lovely book of vouchers, just for you!"

Thank you
for putting up with my bad mood!

I owe you . . .

Thank you for putting up with my bad mood!

I owe you . . .

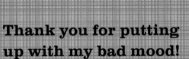

Thank you for putting up with my bad mood!

I owe you . . .

I owe you a ....

....

....

....

I owe you a ....

....

....

....

Voucher given to:
....

Voucher redeemed on:
....

It happened again on:
....

Notes:
....

....

....

Thank you
for doing the shopping!

I owe you . . .

**Thank you
for doing the shopping!**

I owe you . . .

**Thank you
for doing the shopping!**

I owe you . . .

I owe you a ....

....

....

....

I owe you a ....

....

....

....

Voucher given to:

....

Voucher redeemed on:

....

....

It happened again on:

....

Notes:

....

....

Thank you
for breakfast in bed!
I owe you . . .

Thank you
for breakfast in bed!
I owe you . . .

Thank you
for breakfast in bed!
I owe you . . .

I owe you a ....

....

....

....

I owe you a ....

....

....

....

....

....

Voucher given to:
....

Voucher redeemed on:
....

It happened again on:
....

....

Notes:
....

....

....

Thank you
for letting me sleep in!
I owe you . . .

Thanks for letting me sleep!
I owe you . . .

Thanks for letting me sleep!
I owe you . . .

I owe you a

....

....

....

....

I owe you a

....

....

....

....

Voucher given to:

....

....

Voucher redeemed on:

....

....

It happened again on:

....

....

Notes:

....

....

....

Thank you
for everything that you do!
I owe you . . .

**Thank you
for everything you do!**
I owe you . . .

**Thank you
for everything you do!**
I owe you . . .

I owe you a ....
....
....
....
....

I owe you a ....
....
....
....

Voucher given to:
....

....

Voucher redeemed on:
....

....

It happened again on:
....

....

Notes:
....

....

Thank you
for admitting I'm right!

I owe you . . .

Thank you
for admitting I'm right!

I owe you . . .

Thank you
for admitting I'm right!

I owe you . . .

I owe you a
....
....
....
....

I owe you a
....
....
....
....

Voucher given to:
....

Voucher redeemed on:
....

It happened again on:
....

Notes:
....
....
....

Thank you
for pretending to enjoy that!
I owe you . . .

Thanks for pretending to enjoy that!
I owe you . . .

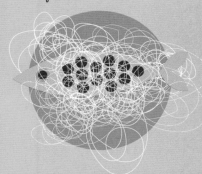

Thanks for pretending to enjoy that!
I owe you . . .

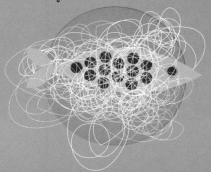

I owe you a
....

....

....

....

I owe you a
....

....

....

....

Voucher given to:
....

Voucher redeemed on:
....

....

It happened again on:
....

Notes:
....

....

Thank you
for a very special day!
I owe you . . .

Thanks
for a special day!
I owe you . . .

Thanks
for a special day!
I owe you . . .

I owe you a ....
....
....
....

I owe you a ....
....
....
....

Voucher given to:
....

Voucher redeemed on:
....

It happened again on:
....

Notes:
....
....

Thank you
for you know what . . .
I owe you . . .

Thank you
for you know what . . .
I owe you . . .

Thank you
for you know what . . .
I owe you . . .

I owe you a

....

....

....

....

I owe you a

....

....

....

....

Voucher given to:

....

Voucher redeemed on:

....

....

It happened again on:

....

Notes:

....

....

....

Thank you
for always being there for me!

I owe you . . .

me ♥ *you*

Thanks
for being there!

I owe you . . .

Thanks
for being there!

I owe you . . .

I owe you a ....
....
....
....
....

I owe you a ....
....
....
....
....

Voucher given to:
....

Voucher redeemed on:
....

It happened again on:
....

Notes:
....
....

Thank you
for my morning coffee!
I owe you . . .

Thank you
for my morning coffee!
I owe you . . .

Thank you
for my morning coffee!
I owe you . . .

I owe you a

....

....

....

....

I owe you a

....

....

....

....

Voucher given to:

....

....

Voucher redeemed on:

....

....

It happened again on:

....

....

Notes:

....

....

....

Thank you
for letting me be me!

I owe you . . .

Thank you
for letting me be me!

I owe you . . .

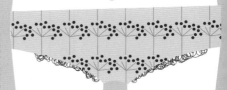

Thank you
for letting me be me!

I owe you . . .

I owe you a ....

....

....

....

....

I owe you a ....

....

....

....

....

Voucher given to:

....

Voucher redeemed on:

....

....

It happened again on:

....

Notes:

....

....

Thank you
for a really fun day out!

I owe you . . .

**Thanks
for a fun day out!**

I owe you . . .

**Thanks
for a fun day out!**

I owe you . . .

I owe you a

....

....

....

....

I owe you a

....

....

....

....

Voucher given to:

....

....

Voucher redeemed on:

....

....

It happened again on:

....

....

Notes:

....

....

Thank you
for loving my keister!

I owe you . . .

**Thanks
for loving my keister!**

I owe you . . .

**Thanks
for loving my keister!**

I owe you . . .

I owe you a ....

....

....

....

I owe you a ....

....

....

....

Voucher given to:

....

Voucher redeemed on:

....

It happened again on:

....

Notes:

....

....

....

Thank you
for being there for all of us!

I owe you . . .

**Thank you
for being there for us!**

I owe you . . .

**Thank you
for being there for us!**

I owe you . . .

I owe you a ....
....
....
....
....

I owe you a ....
....
....
....

Voucher given to:
....
....

Voucher redeemed on:
....
....

It happened again on:
....
....

Notes:
....
....
....

Thank you
for taking out the trash!
I owe you . . .

Thanks
for taking out the trash!
I owe you . . .

Thanks
for taking out the trash!
I owe you . . .

I owe you a ....
....
....
....
....

I owe you a ....
....
....
....

Voucher given to:
....

Voucher redeemed on:
....

It happened again on:
....

Notes:
....
....
....

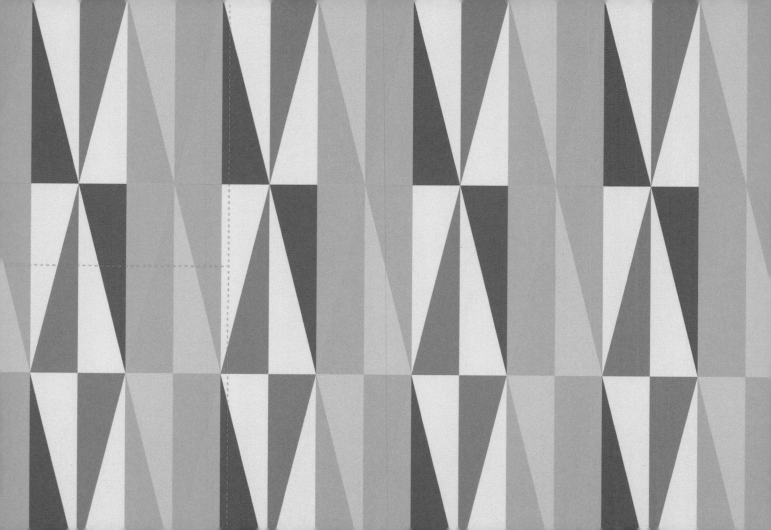

Sorry, but there's this
crazy new invention called a hanger . . .
You owe me . . .

Sorry, but there's this crazy new thing called a hanger . . .
You owe me . . .

Sorry, but there's this crazy new thing called a hanger . . .
You owe me . . .

You owe me a ....

....

....

....

You owe me a ....

....

....

....

Voucher given to:

....

....

Voucher redeemed on:

....

....

It happened again on:

....

....

Notes:

....

....

Sorry I've been so busy!

I'll make it up to you . . .

I owe you . . .

Sorry I've been so busy!

I owe you . . .

Sorry I've been so busy!

I owe you . . .

I owe you a ....

....

....

....

....

I owe you a ....

....

....

....

....

Voucher given to:
....

....

Voucher redeemed on:
....

....

It happened again on:
....

....

Notes:
....

....

....

Sorry to say this honey...
but you need some manscaping!

You owe me...

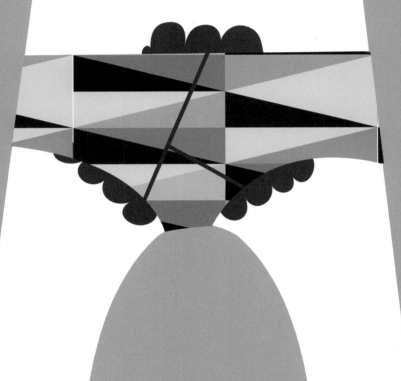

Sorry, but you need a trim!

You owe me...

Sorry, but you need a trim!

You owe me...

You owe me a ....

....

....

....

You owe me a ....

....

....

....

Voucher given to: ....

....

Voucher redeemed on: ....

....

It happened again on: ....

....

Notes: ....

....

....

Sorry I used your razor!
But now I have very smooth legs ...

I owe you ...

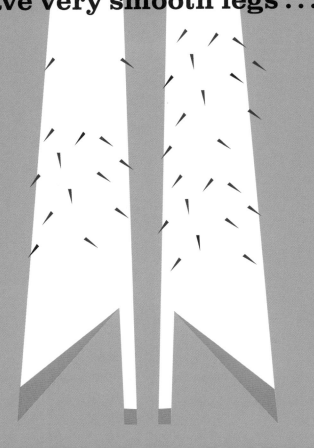

Sorry I used your razor.
But now I have sexy legs!

I owe you ...

Sorry I used your razor.
But now I have sexy legs!

I owe you ...

I owe you a ....

....

....

....

I owe you a ....

....

....

....

Voucher given to:

....

....

Voucher redeemed on:

....

....

It happened again on:

....

....

Notes:

....

....

....

Sorry I ate the chocolate!

I'll buy more tomorrow ...

I owe you ...

Sorry I ate all the chocolate ...

I owe you ...

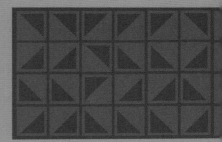

Sorry I ate all the chocolate ...

I owe you ...

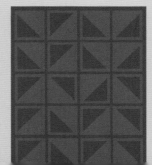

I owe you a
....
....
....
....

I owe you a
....
....
....
....

Voucher given to:
....

Voucher redeemed on:
....

It happened again on:
....

Notes:
....
....

Sorry I'm not perfect!

But we all have our imperfections . . .

I owe you . . .

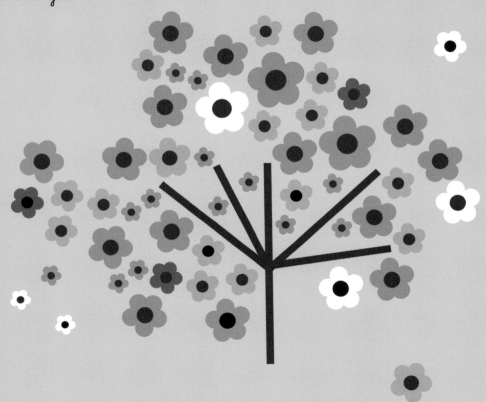

Sorry, I know I'm not perfect!

I owe you . . .

Sorry, I know I'm not perfect!

I owe you . . .

I owe you a

....

....

....

....

Voucher given to:

....

Voucher redeemed on:

....

It happened again on:

....

Notes:

....

....

I owe you a

....

....

Sorry I talk so much!

I'll shut up now.

I owe you . . .

Sorry I talk so much!

I owe you . . .

Sorry I talk so much!

I owe you . . .

I owe you a ....

....

....

....

I owe you a ....

....

....

....

Voucher given to:
....

....

Voucher redeemed on:
....

....

It happened again on:
....

....

Notes:
....

....

....

Sorry I'm such a grump!

I've got nothing to wear.

I owe you . . .

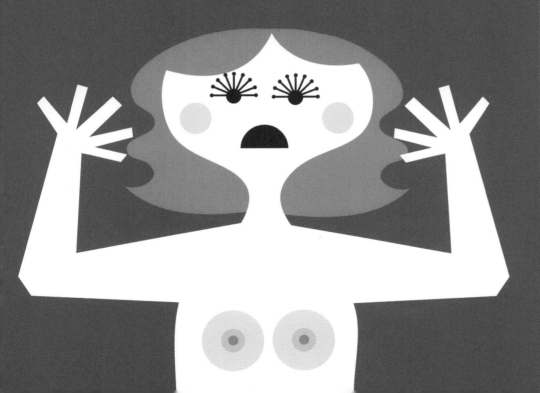

Sorry I'm grumpy but I've got nothing to wear!

I owe you . . .

Sorry I'm grumpy but I've got nothing to wear!

I owe you . . .

I owe you a ....
....
....
....

I owe you a ....
....
....
....

Voucher given to:
....
....

Voucher redeemed on:
....
....

It happened again on:
....
....

Notes:
....
....
....

Sorry I fell asleep on you!

I owe you . . .

Sorry I fell asleep . . .

I owe you . . .

Sorry I fell asleep . . .

I owe you . . .

I owe you a ....

....

....

....

....

I owe you a ....

....

....

....

....

Voucher given to:

....

Voucher redeemed on:

....

....

It happened again on:

....

Notes:

....

....

....

Sorry I scratched

the car, dear!

I owe you . . .

Sorry I scratched the car!

I owe you . . .

Sorry I scratched the car!

I owe you . . .

I owe you a ....

....

....

....

I owe you a ....

....

....

....

Voucher given to:

....

Voucher redeemed on:

....

It happened again on:

....

Notes:

....

....

Sorry honey, but you stink!
Perhaps it's time for a shower . . .

You owe me . . .

Sorry honey, but you stink! Please shower!

You owe me . . .

Sorry honey, but you stink! Please shower!

You owe me . . .

You owe me a ....

....

....

....

You owe me a ....

....

....

....

Voucher given to:

....

....

Voucher redeemed on:

....

....

It happened again on:

....

....

Notes:

....

....

....

Sorry I was too tired . . .

I'll be up for it next time!

I owe you . . .

I owe you a ....
....
....
....
....

I owe you a ....
....
....
....
....

Voucher given to:
....

Voucher redeemed on:
....

It happened again on:
....

Notes:
....
....
....

Sorry for being late!
(Again...)

I owe you...

Sorry I was late!
(Again...)

I owe you...

Sorry I was late!
(Again...)

I owe you...

I owe you a

....

....

....

I owe you a

....

....

....

....

Voucher given to:

....

Voucher redeemed on:

....

It happened again on:

....

Notes:

....

....

....

Sorry I snapped . . .
I'll make it up to you!

I owe you . . .

Sorry I snapped . . .
I'll make it up to you!

I owe you . . .

Sorry I snapped . . .
I'll make it up to you!

I owe you . . .

I owe you a ....
....
....
....

I owe you a ....
....
....
....

Voucher given to:
....
....

Voucher redeemed on:
....
....

It happened again on:
....
....

Notes:
....
....
....

Sorry I spent so much!

I owe you . . .

Sorry I spent so much!

I owe you . . .

Sorry I spent so much!

I owe you . . .

I owe you a

....

....

....

....

I owe you a

....

....

....

....

Voucher given to:

....

....

Voucher redeemed on:

....

....

It happened again on:

....

....

Notes:

....

....

....

Sorry you have to
put up with my crazy family!

I owe you . . .

Sorry you have to put up with my family!

I owe you . . .

Sorry you have to put up with my family!

I owe you . . .

I owe you a ....
....
....
....
....

I owe you a ....
....
....
....

Voucher given to:
....
....

Voucher redeemed on:
....
....

It happened again on:
....
....

Notes:
....
....
....

Sorry I got so tipsy!

I owe you . . .

Sorry I got so tipsy!

I owe you . . .

Sorry I got so tipsy!

I owe you . . .

I owe you

....

....

....

....

I owe you

....

....

....

....

Voucher given to:

....

Voucher redeemed on:

....

It happened again on:

....

Notes:

....

....

if you . . .

If you leave
stuff on the stairs again ...

You owe me ...

If you leave stuff on the stairs again ...

You owe me ...

If you leave stuff on the stairs again ...

You owe me ...

You owe me

....

....

....

You owe me

....

....

....

Voucher given to:

....

Voucher redeemed on:

....

It happened again on:

....

Notes:

....

....

If you belch

at the table one more time . . .

You owe me . . .

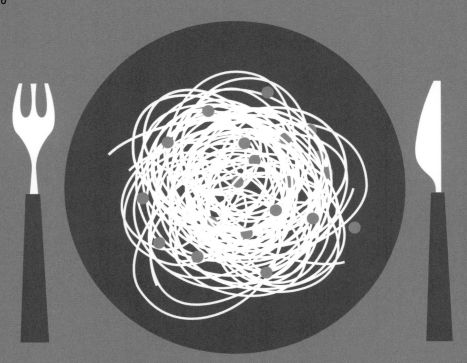

If you belch at the table again . . .

You owe me . . .

If you belch at the table again . . .

You owe me . . .

You owe me ....

....

....

....

You owe me ....

....

....

....

Voucher given to:
....

....

Voucher redeemed on:
....

....

It happened again on:
....

....

Notes:
....

....

....

If you don't take me out
soon, someone else might . . .
You owe me . . .

If you don't take me out soon, someone else might . . .

You owe me . . .

If you don't take me out soon, someone else might . . .

You owe me . . .

You owe me

....

....

....

You owe me

....

....

....

Voucher given to:

....

....

Voucher redeemed on:

....

....

It happened again on:

....

....

Notes:

....

....

....

If you're late again,
you owe me a treat . . .

If you're late again, it'll cost you . . .

You owe me . . .

If you're late again, it'll cost you . . .

You owe me . . .

You owe me

....

....

....

....

You owe me

....

....

....

....

Voucher given to:

....

....

Voucher redeemed on:

....

....

It happened again on:

....

....

Notes:

....

....

If you don't
wipe the seat . . .
You owe me a pair of shoes each time!

**If you don't wipe
the seat . . .**

You owe me a pair of new shoes!

**If you don't wipe
the seat . . .**

You owe me a pair of new shoes!

You owe me ....

....

....

....

You owe me ....

....

....

....

Voucher given to:

....

Voucher redeemed on:

....

It happened again on:

....

Notes:

....

....

If you forget,

I get to boss you around all day . . .

If you forget, I get to boss you around all day . . .

If you forget, I get to boss you around all day . . .

You owe me

....

....

....

....

You owe me

....

....

....

....

Voucher given to:

....

....

Voucher redeemed on:

....

....

It happened again on:

....

....

Notes:

....

....

....

If I have to pick up one
more sock, I'll stick it in your mouth!

If I have to pick up
one more sock...

You owe me...

If I have to pick up
one more sock...

You owe me...

You owe me
....
....
....
....

You owe me
....
....
....
....

Voucher given to:
....

Voucher redeemed on:
....
....

It happened again on:
....

Notes:
....
....
....

If you leave your dirty
underwear lying around again . . .
You owe me . . .

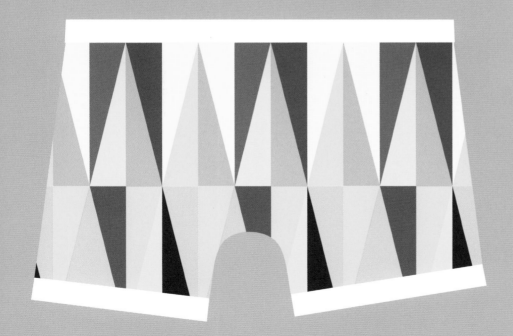

If you leave your dirty undies lying around . . .
You owe me . . .

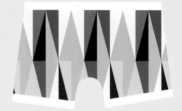

If you leave your dirty undies lying around . . .
You owe me . . .

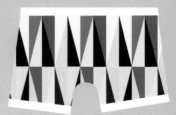

You owe me ....

....

....

....

You owe me ....

....

....

....

Voucher given to: ....

....

Voucher redeemed on: ....

....

It happened again on: ....

....

Notes: ....

....

....

If you do something,
please do it properly!
You owe me . . .

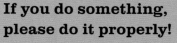

**If you do something,
please do it properly!**
You owe me . . .

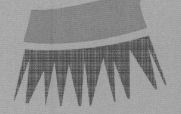

**If you do something,
please do it properly!**
You owe me . . .

You owe me

....

....

....

....

You owe me

....

....

....

....

Voucher given to:

....

....

Voucher redeemed on:

....

....

It happened again on:

....

....

Notes:

....

....

If you don't stop fiddling
with your apps and gadgets ...
You owe me ...

If you don't turn off your gadgets ...
You owe me ...

You owe me

....

....

....

You owe me

....

....

....

Voucher given to:

....

....

Voucher redeemed on:

....

....

It happened again on:

....

....

Notes:

....

....

If you mention your
mother one more time . . .

You owe me . . .

If you mention your
mother one more time . . .

You owe me . . .

If you mention your
mother one more time . . .

You owe me . . .

You owe me ....

....

....

....

You owe me ....

....

....

....

Voucher given to:

....

Voucher redeemed on:

....

It happened again on:

....

Notes:

....

....

If you're not occupied . . .
do you want to get busy?

You owe me . . .

If you're not occupied . . . want to get busy?

You owe me . . .

If you're not occupied . . . want to get busy?

You owe me . . .

I owe you ....

....

....

....

I owe you ....

....

....

....

Voucher given to:
....

Voucher redeemed on:
....

It happened again on:
....

Notes:
....

....

....

If I haven't done the
laundry, why don't you?

You owe me . . .

If I haven't done the
laundry, maybe
you should!

You owe me . . .

If I haven't done the
laundry, maybe
you should!

You owe me . . .

You owe me

....

....

....

You owe me

....

....

....

Voucher given to:

....

Voucher redeemed on:

....

It happened again on:

....

Notes:

....

....

If you act like you're
dying every time you catch a cold ...

You owe me ...

If you act like you're dying because of a cold ...

You owe me ...

If you act like you're dying because of a cold ...

You owe me ...

You owe me ....

....

....

....

You owe me

....

....

....

Voucher given to:

....

Voucher redeemed on:

....

It happened again on:

....

Notes:

....

....

If life gives you lemons,
make a margarita!

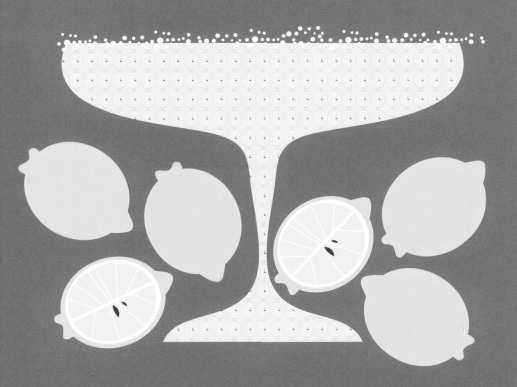

If life gives you lemons,
make a margarita!

If life gives you lemons,
make a margarita!

You owe me
....
....
....
....

You owe me
....
....
....
....

Voucher given to:
....

Voucher redeemed on:
....

It happened again on:
....

Notes:
....
....
....

If you don't start listening to me, I might think you don't care . . .

You owe me . . .

If you don't listen to me, I'll be sad!

You owe me . . .

If you don't listen to me, I'll be sad!

You owe me . . .

You owe me ....

....

....

....

....

You owe me ....

....

....

....

Voucher given to:
....

....

Voucher redeemed on:
....

....

It happened again on:
....

....

Notes:
....

....

....

If you clog the drain
one more time . . .

You owe me . . .

If you clog the drain one more time . . .

You owe me . . .

If you clog the drain one more time . . .

You owe me . . .

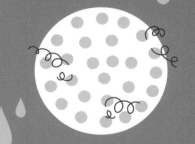

You owe me ....

....

....

....

You owe me ....

....

....

....

Voucher given to:

....

Voucher redeemed on:

....

It happened again on:

....

Notes:

....

....

....

more...

**Oh, brother!
Not again!**

You owe me . . .

**Ugh, you farted.
Again!**

You owe me . . .

I had a really bad day . . .

*Would you mind cooking
tonight, dear?*

**Seriously honey?
What the heck!**

You owe me . . .

I don't feel like cooking.

Let's order takeout!

**Sweetie, please . . .
stop talking!**

You owe me . . .

Please stop stealing my candy! Get your own!

Please can you trim the hedges?

Can you please pick up some groceries?

Please take it easy tonight!

Please stop sprinkling on the toilet seat!

Will you please run me a bubble bath?

**Thanks for making such
an effort!**

I owe you . . .

**Thanks for helping out
around the house!**

I owe you . . .

**Thanks for always
making me feel better!**

I owe you . . .

**Thanks for letting me
hog the remote!**

I owe you . . .

**Thanks for letting me
shower first!**

I owe you . . .

**Thanks for warming up
the bed for me!**

I owe you . . .

Thanks for giving up your poker night for me!

I owe you . . .

Thanks for coming home early!

I owe you . . .

Thanks for making me so happy every day!

I owe you . . .

Thanks for giving me more closet space!

I owe you . . .

Thanks for loving me when I least deserve it!

I owe you . . .

Thanks for putting up with me and my oddities!

I owe you . . .

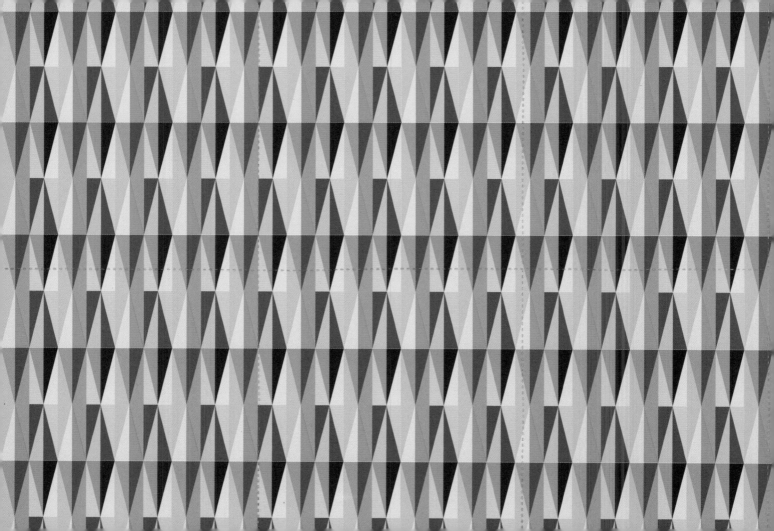

Sorry for laughing at you!
I owe you . . .

Sorry for not being a better listener!
I owe you . . .

Sorry I burned dinner . . .
I owe you . . .

Sorry for not paying attention to you!
I owe you . . .

Sorry I didn't love your gift . . . I know you tried!
I owe you . . .

Sorry I made plans without you . . .
I owe you . . .

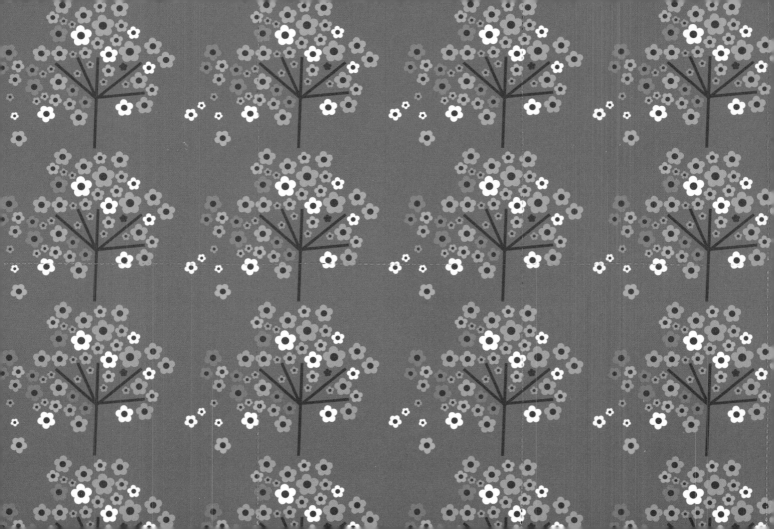

Sorry I don't like watching sports.

I owe you . . .

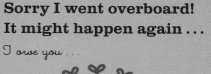

Sorry for waking you up!

I owe you . . .

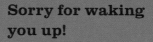

Sorry I went overboard! It might happen again . . .

I owe you . . .

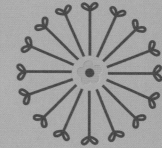

Sorry for throwing that away!

I owe you . . .

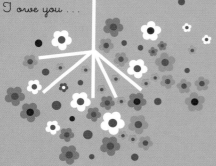

Sorry for insisting we do it my way!

I owe you . . .

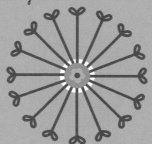

Sorry for being a bit unreasonable sometimes!

I owe you . . .

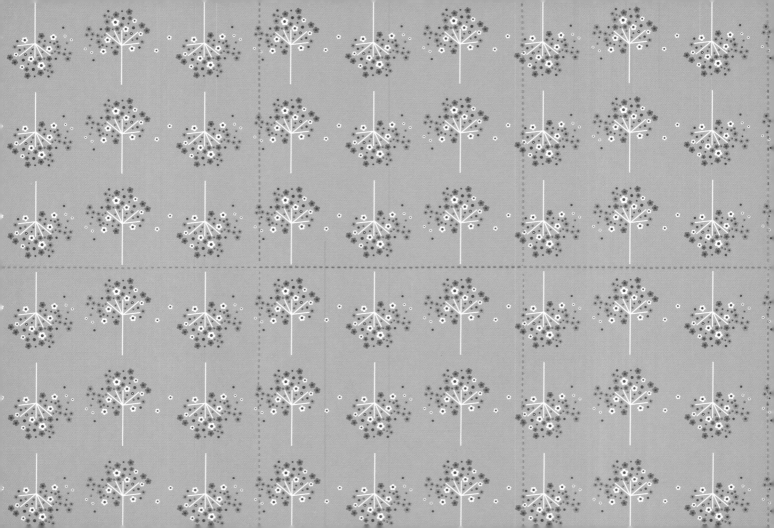

If you don't change the sheets soon . . .

You owe me . . .

If you eavesdrop on my conversations . . .

You owe me . . .

If you don't organize your junk . . .

You owe me . . .

If you don't say sorry . . . I won't forgive you!

You owe me . . .

If you don't cut your toenails . . .

You owe me . . .

If you don't brush your teeth before you kiss me . . .

You owe me . . .

If you leave your stuff lying around . . .

You owe me . . .

If you don't fix that thing soon . . . .

You owe me . . .

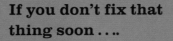

If you pretend to be asleep again . . .

You owe me . . .

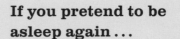

If you hog all the hot water . . .

You owe me . . .

If you don't hang up your wet towel . . .

You owe me . . .

If you leave your cup in the sink again . . .

You owe me . . .

The rights to this book have been negotiated
by the literary agency Sea of Stories,
www.seaofstories.com

Concept: Snor publishers
Text and illustrations: Sandra Isaksson
Dutch-language Editor: Suzanne de Boer
Layout: Studio 100% and en-publique.nl
Translation: The Language Lab

With thanks to Gerard Janssen.
A special thank you also goes out to
Kees and Willemien. (You both know why.)

ISBN: 978-160106629-9
UPC: 825703310542

10 9 8 7 6 5 4 3 2 1